The New FIRE ENGINE

Story and
Pictures by —

JAY HYDE BARNUM

William Morrow and Company
New York   1952

Above the door of the new
firehouse two men were hanging
a sign.

3

They were getting ready for
the new pumper fire engine,
and the very next day it arrived.
All the children, with their
dogs and cats, and other village
people came to see it. The ten

firemen of Engine Company
Number 3 were there—proud of
their new rubber coats and
boots and hats. But they were
even prouder of their new fire
engine.

Ed Walsh, the captain, started up the motor. It sounded very strong. Several firemen connected the suction hose to the fire hydrant, while others pulled out lengths of hose from the truck and attached the nozzle.

Suddenly the big hose filled with water, as Ed shoved the pump lever into pumping gear. Out shot a stream of water.

The children yelled, the dogs barked, the cats meowed, and all the people cheered. "What a fine fire engine!" everyone said.

Engine Number 3 was very proud of itself.

Early one morning the fire whistle blew. Three long blasts —two short, over and over again. The door of Engine Company Number 3 flew open, and in rushed the firemen.

The motor started with a
great roar. Out of the door
leaped Engine Number 3, its
siren screaming.

Wheee—Whoooo—eeee, it went,
as loud as it could.

The fire was way out on the very edge of Littleton. Smoke and flames were pouring out of an empty barn. There were no fire hydrants anywhere near, so Ed Walsh pulled up beside a brook. The firemen connected the two lengths of the big suction hose and lowered one end into the brook.

By this time other fire engines had arrived. Ed speeded up the motor to start sucking water from the brook into the pump.

The long hose started to fill
with water and then stopped.
Not even a drop came out of the
nozzle.

Ed knew what had happened. "Jim," he shouted, "check those valves! We're sucking air somewhere."

The firemen were getting more and more excited, because the other engines had started to throw streams of water on the barn. Engine Number 3 was excited, itself. This was its first chance to show what it could do.

Now the other fire engines were getting the flames under control, and not one drop of water had Engine Number 3 been able to throw on the fire. Engine Number 3 was very much upset.

At last the men managed to
find what was wrong, but by
that time it was just too late.
The fire was out.

"Some fire engine you've got there, fellows," called a man in the crowd. A loud roar of laughter followed.

The crew were angry as could be, and Engine Number 3 felt simply awful.

It was weeks later before the fire whistle blew again. Ed Walsh, who lived next door, was the first to arrive. He jumped into the driver's seat and pressed the starter.

Brrrr, it went. Then *Brrr—br —br—b* . . . Then nothing more.

"Hey! Who checked those batteries last?" Ed called out.

"I was supposed to," Allan Jones said, "but I had to go

away. Ned said he'd take care of it for me."

"Ned's sick," said Tom.

"Well!" Ed exclaimed in disgust. "You fellows better get busy and push, and make it snappy. We're supposed to be going to a fire."

The firemen all pushed, and Engine Number 3 was soon headed down the street. They pushed and pushed and pushed.

Finally
they came
to a downgrade,
and the motor let
out a great *bang-bang*,
and clouds of black smoke
poured out of the exhaust. Engine
Number 3 was on its way at last!

But just as they reached the main street, a policeman rushed out, waving at them to stop. Then they heard the signal, "Fire's out." Engine Number 3 was very sad. It had wanted so much to show what it could do.

Weeks and weeks went by. It was winter now, with snow and sleet and ice and cold. Engine Number 3 had double wheels and tires on the rear axle to give it more strength and pulling power. The special chains for these wheels had not yet come. So there were chains only on the two outside rear wheels.

One night, while it was snowing hard, the fire whistle began to blow. A house at the very top of a long steep hill was on fire.

Engine Number 3
roared out of the
firehouse and raced for the hill.

Up, up and UP it went, its chains clanking. But slower and *slower* and s-l-o-w-e-r turned its wheels as the snow got deeper and the hill steeper. Ed Walsh shoved into a lower gear, but the wheels started to spin. Then Engine Number 3 slid backward into the ditch.

The firemen
shoveled and
pushed and pulled,
as Ed tried to drive
up out of the ditch, but
the wheels kept spinning in
the snow. As the other fire
engines pulled up the steep hill,
their crews shouted at the men
of Engine Number 3. "Why
don't you sell that for junk?"

Engine Number 3 felt sick. It knew that it could have sailed up that hill as easy as pie with the proper chains on its rear wheels.

After that, whenever Engine Number 3 was taken out for drill, people laughed and joked about

it. Poor Engine Number 3 could hardly bear it.

Now the weather was getting warm again, and still the new fire engine had no chance to prove that it could do a good job. There wasn't a single fire.

Then one day Engine Number 3 overheard a boy talking outside the firehouse. "Did you hear about the parade—soldiers, guns, fire engines, and everything? And they're going to let kids ride on the fire engines too."

"Not us, though," said a little girl. "Daddy said they weren't going to let our fire engine be in the parade. He said probably it would break down."

"Why do we have such a piece of junk?" said another boy.

As the children left, Engine Number 3 felt worse than ever before. It began to cry—right into its muffler.

When the crew heard that their engine was not going to be in the parade, they were very angry. They held a meeting to talk things over. "Fellows," said Ed, "we all know there's nothing wrong with our fire engine. The things that happened were not Engine Number 3's fault at all. We are to blame. This was a new job for us. But with all the drilling we've done now, we can do our job and do it right. We can prove to everyone that we have a fine fire engine."

All the firemen cheered and clapped, and Engine Number 3 felt much better. But days passed and nothing happened.

Then on the night before the parade, the fire whistle started to blow and blow and BLOW! Everyone knew it must be a very big fire, and it was—a three-story apartment house.

Almost before the firehouse door was open, Engine Number 3 was off.

The firemen had to run and jump aboard as it swung out into the street, its siren shrieking. Faster and faster it went.

All the children, with their dogs and cats, and other people of the village followed.

But Engine Number 3 left
everyone far behind. It was
going so fast that the firemen

couldn't even keep their feet on
the running boards. They had to
hang on by their hands.

Before Engine Number 3 even stopped, its crew had the long hose out. Soon the new fire engine was throwing great streams of water on the raging flames, before any of the other engines had arrived. Suddenly a shout was heard, and people began pointing. At one of the top windows a shaggy head with long ears appeared. It was a dog, trapped in the roaring flames.

A long extension ladder from the hook-and-ladder truck was

run up to the
third floor, and a
fireman started
to climb up the

ladder. But just
then flames burst
out of the win-
dows above him.

The crew of Engine Number 3 sent up powerful streams of water to protect the fireman so he could reach the dog. In a flash he had it in his arms and hurried back down the ladder.

Soon the fire was brought under control with the help of all the fire engines. As Engine Number 3 started for home, its bell clanging loudly, the crowd cheered.

Engine Number 3 was so happy, well, it was so happy it was sure it would blow a gasket. But it didn't, not quite.

That night, while the crew were cleaning and polishing Engine Number 3, the telephone rang. Ed answered, and a broad grin spread over his face. "Hey, fellows," he called, as he hung up, "that was the mayor, inviting our fire engine to lead the parade tomorrow!"

The next day, the parade
started down the street, led by

the band. Next came the Girl
Scouts and the Boy Scouts; and

then came Engine Number 3!
The children, with their dogs

and cats, were riding on it,
waving flags and singing!

47

From that time on, nothing ever went wrong with Engine Number 3. Its crew always knew just what to do and they did it.

So did the new fire engine!